play guitar with...

coldplay

play guitar with...

coldplay

Wise Publications
part of The Music Sales Group

London/New York/Paris/Sydney/Copenhagen/Berlin/Madrid/Tokyo

Published by
Wise Publications
8/9 Frith Street,
London W1D 3JB, England

Exclusive Distributors:
Music Sales Limited
Distribution Centre, Newmarket Road,
Bury St Edmunds, Suffolk IP33 3YB
Music Sales Pty Limited
120 Rothschild Avenue,
Rosebery, NSW 2018, Australia

Order No. AM978098
ISBN 1-84449-182-X
This book © Copyright 2003
by Wise Publications

Compiled by Nick Crispin
Music arranged by Arthur Dick
Music processed by Paul Ewers Music Design
Cover designed by Fresh Lemon
Cover photograph courtesy of London Features International
Printed in the United Kingdom by
Caligraving Limited, Thetford, Norfolk

CD recorded by Gilles Ruppert
Mixed and mastered by Jonas Persson
All guitars by Arthur Dick
Bass by Paul Townsend
Drums by Brett Morgan

Your Guarantee of Quality

As publishers, we strive to produce
every book to the highest commercial standards.
The music has been freshly engraved and the book has
been carefully designed to minimise awkward page turns
and to make playing from it a real pleasure.
Particular care has been given to specifying acid-free,
neutral-sized paper made from pulps which have not been
elemental chlorine bleached. This pulp is from farmed
sustainable forests and was produced with
special regard for the environment.
Throughout, the printing and binding have been planned
to ensure a sturdy, attractive publication which
should give years of enjoyment.
If your copy fails to meet our high standards,
please inform us and we will gladly replace it.

www.musicsales.com

guitar tablature explained

Guitar music can be notated in three different ways: on a musical stave, in tablature, and in rhythm slashes.

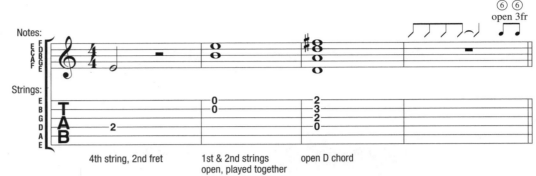

RHYTHM SLASHES are written above the stave. Strum chords in the rhythm indicated. Round noteheads indicate single notes.

THE MUSICAL STAVE shows pitches and rhythms and is divided by lines into bars. Pitches are named after the first seven letters of the alphabet.

TABLATURE graphically represents the guitar fingerboard. Each horizontal line represents a string, and each number represents a fret.

4th string, 2nd fret

1st & 2nd strings open, played together

open D chord

definitions for special guitar notation

SEMI-TONE BEND: Strike the note and bend up a semi-tone (1/2 step).

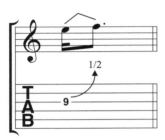

WHOLE-TONE BEND: Strike the note and bend up a whole-tone (whole step).

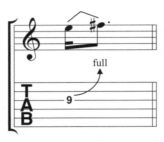

GRACE NOTE BEND: Strike the note and bend as indicated. Play the first note as quickly as possible.

QUARTER-TONE BEND: Strike the note and bend up a 1/4 step.

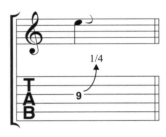

BEND & RELEASE: Strike the note and bend up as indicated, then release back to the original note.

COMPOUND BEND & RELEASE: Strike the note and bend up and down in the rhythm indicated.

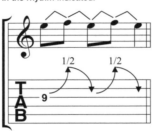

PRE-BEND: Bend the note as indicated, then strike it.

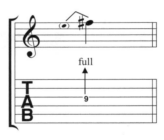

PRE-BEND & RELEASE: Bend the note as indicated. Strike it and release the note back to the original pitch.

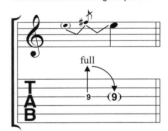

UNISON BEND: Strike the two notes simultaneously and bend the lower note up to the pitch of the higher.

BEND & RESTRIKE: Strike the note and bend as indicated then restrike the string where the symbol occurs.

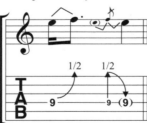

BEND, HOLD AND RELEASE: Same as bend and release but hold the bend for the duration of the tie.

BEND AND TAP: Bend the note as indicated and tap the higher fret while still holding the bend.

VIBRATO: The string is vibrated by rapidly bending and releasing the note with the fretting hand.

HAMMER-ON: Strike the first note with one finger, then sound the second note (on the same string) with another finger by fretting it without picking.

PULL-OFF: Place both fingers on the notes to be sounded, strike the first note and without picking, pull the finger off to sound the second note.

LEGATO SLIDE (GLISS): Strike the first note and then slide the same fret-hand finger up or down to the second note. The second note is not struck.

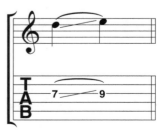

NOTE: The speed of any bend is indicated by the music notation and tempo.

SHIFT SLIDE (GLISS & RESTRIKE): Same as legato slide, except the second note is struck.

TRILL: Very rapidly alternate between the notes indicated by continuously hammering on and pulling off.

TAPPING: Hammer ("tap") the fret indicated with the pick-hand index or middle finger and pull off to the note fretted by the fret hand.

PICK SCRAPE: The edge of the pick is rubbed down (or up) the string, producing a scratchy sound.

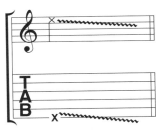

MUFFLED STRINGS: A percussive sound is produced by laying the fret hand across the string(s) without depressing, and striking them with the pick hand.

NATURAL HARMONIC: Strike the note while the fret-hand lightly touches the string directly over the fret indicated.

PINCH HARMONIC: The note is fretted normally and a harmonic is produced by adding the edge of the thumb or the tip of the index finger of the pick hand to the normal pick attack.

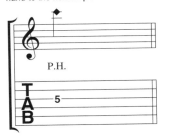

HARP HARMONIC: The note is fretted normally and a harmonic is produced by gently resting the pick hand's index finger directly above the indicated fret (in brackets) while plucking the appropriate string.

PALM MUTING: The note is partially muted by the pick hand lightly touching the string(s) just before the bridge.

RAKE: Drag the pick across the strings indicated with a single motion.

TREMOLO PICKING: The note is picked as rapidly and continuously as possible.

ARPEGGIATE: Play the notes of the chord indicated by quickly rolling them from bottom to top.

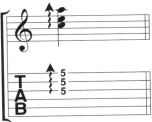

SWEEP PICKING: Rhythmic downstroke and/or upstroke motion across the strings.

VIBRATO DIVE BAR AND RETURN: The pitch of the note or chord is dropped a specific number of steps (in rhythm) then returned to the original pitch.

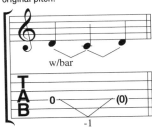

VIBRATO BAR SCOOP: Depress the bar just before striking the note, then quickly release the bar.

VIBRATO BAR DIP: Strike the note and then immediately drop a specific number of steps, then release back to the original pitch.

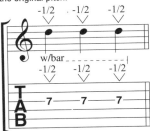

additional musical definitions

	*(accent)*	• Accentuate note (play it louder).
	(accent)	• Accentuate note with great intensity.
	(staccato)	• Shorten time value of note.
∎		• Downstroke
V		• Upstroke

NOTE: Tablature numbers in brackets mean:
1. The note is sustained, but a new articulation (such as hammer on or slide) begins.
2. A note may be fretted but not necessarily played.

D.%. al Coda

• Go back to the sign (%), then play until the bar marked *To Coda* ⊕ then skip to the section marked ⊕ *Coda*.

D.C. al Fine

• Go back to the beginning of the song and play until the bar marked *Fine*.

tacet

• Instrument is silent (drops out).

• Repeat bars between signs.

1. **2.**

• When a repeated section has different endings, play the first ending only the first time and the second ending only the second time.

7

don't panic

Words & Music by Guy Berryman, Jon Buckland, Will Champion & Chris Martin

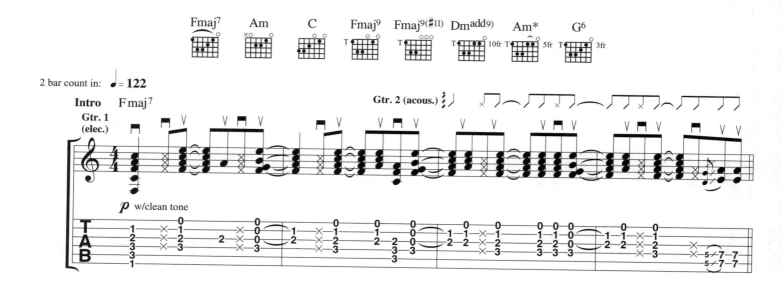

high speed

Words & Music by Guy Berryman, Jon Buckland, Will Champion & Chris Martin

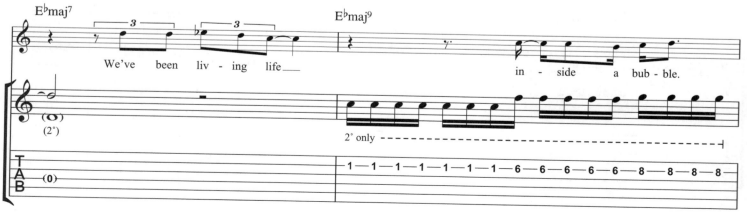

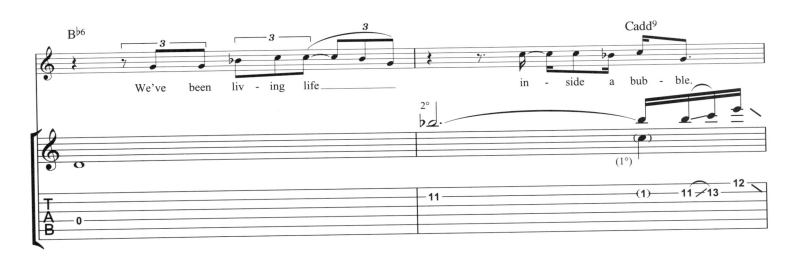

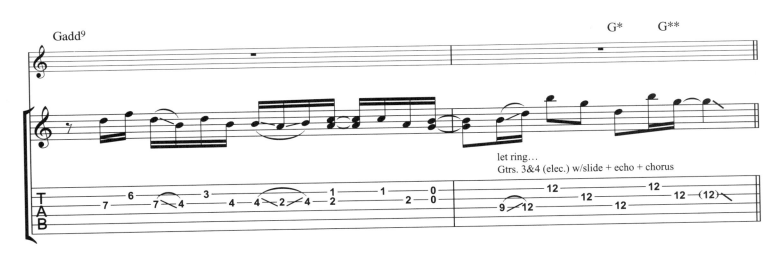

Chorus

in my place

Words & Music by Guy Berryman, Jon Buckland, Will Champion & Chris Martin

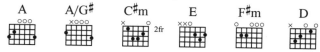

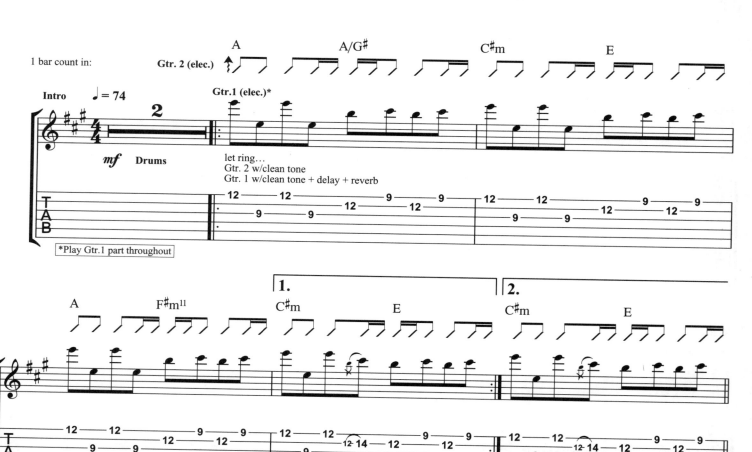

god put a smile upon your face

Words & Music by Guy Berryman, Jon Buckland, Will Champion & Chris Martin

*basic chord names

Play Gtr. 3 throughout

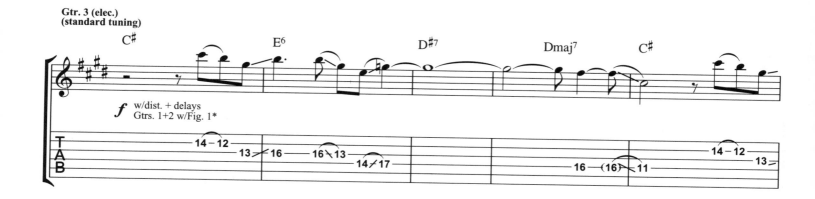

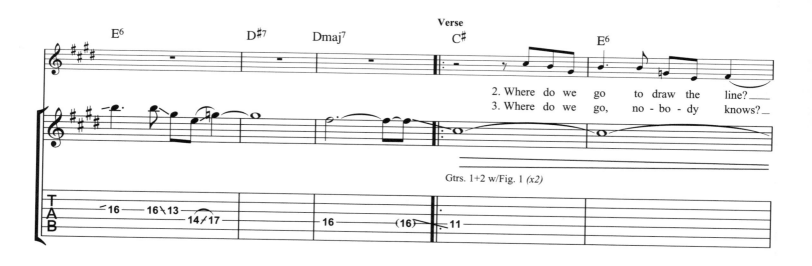

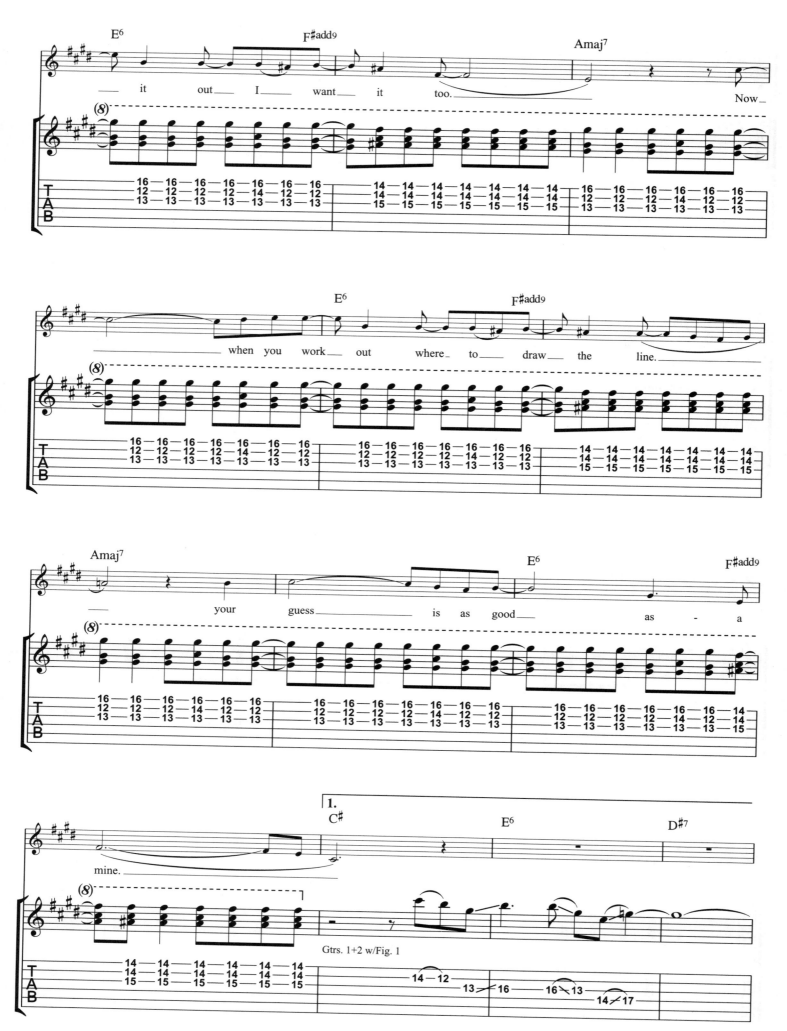

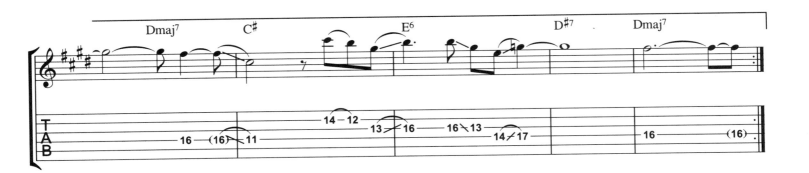

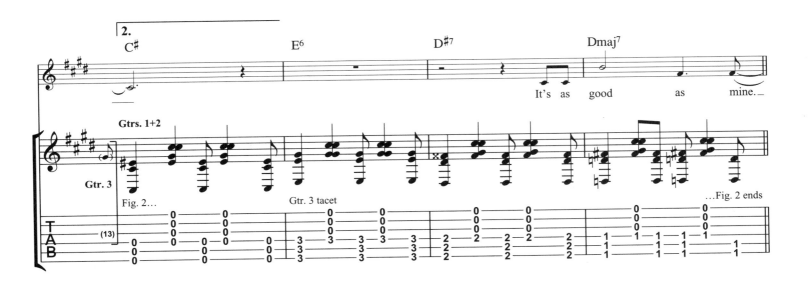

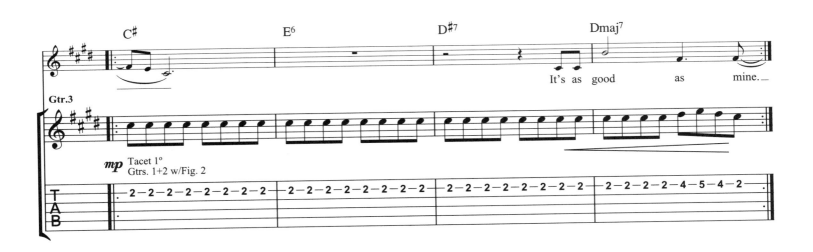

shiver

Words & Music by Guy Berryman, Jon Buckland, Will Champion & Chris Martin

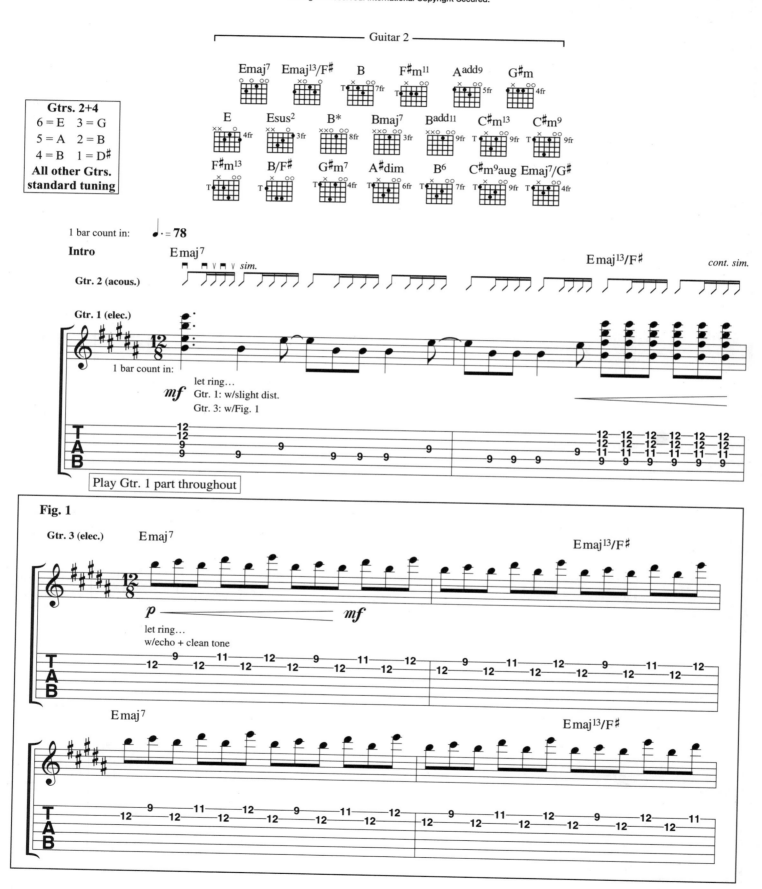

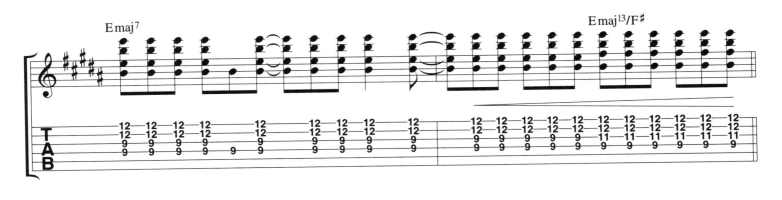

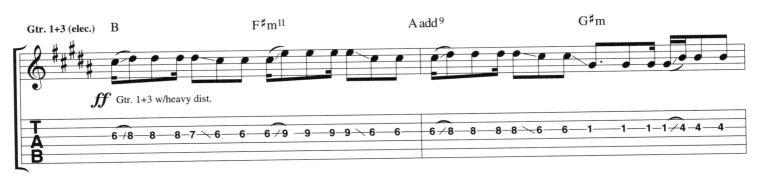

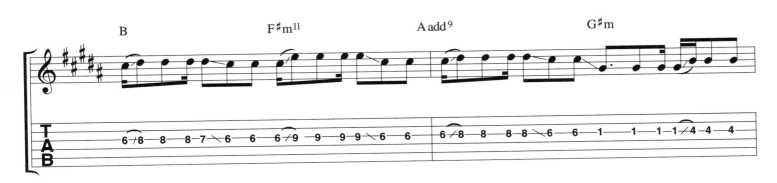

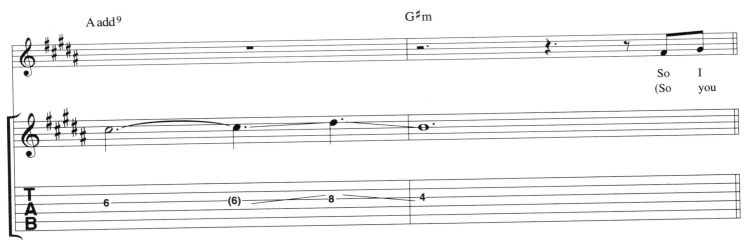

Pre-chorus

from the mo - ment I wake,___ to the mo - ment I sleep,___

I'll be there by your side,___ just you try and stop me.___

Fig. 2

Gtr. 3

w/slight dist.

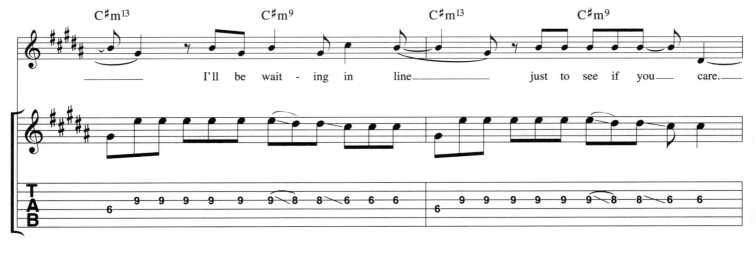

I'll be wait - ing in line_____ just to see if you___ care.___

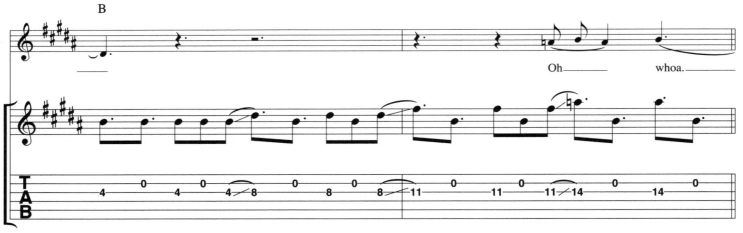

Oh_____ whoa.___

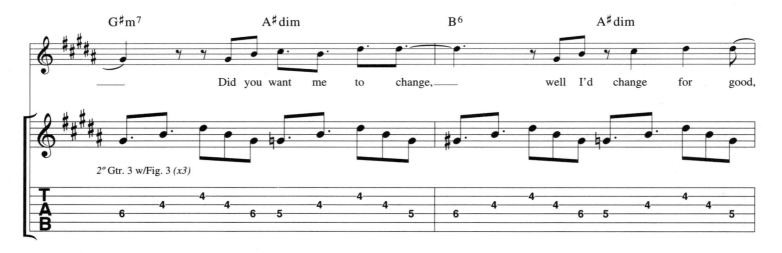

Did you want me to change,___ well I'd change for good,

2° Gtr. 3 w/Fig. 3 (x3)

Fig. 3

Gtr. 3

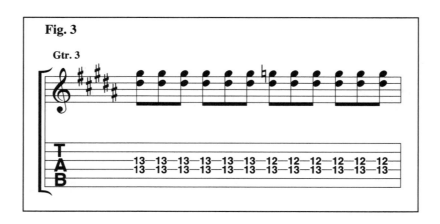

and I want you to know___ that you'll al - ways___ get your

2° Gtr. 3 w/Fig. 4

way. I want - ed to___ say,___ don't you shi - ver,___

w/bar

Chorus

shi - ver,___

Gtrs. 1&3

ff w/heavy dist.

Fig. 4

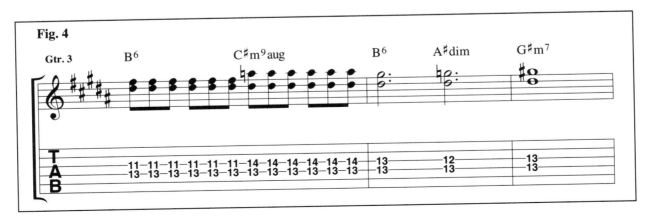

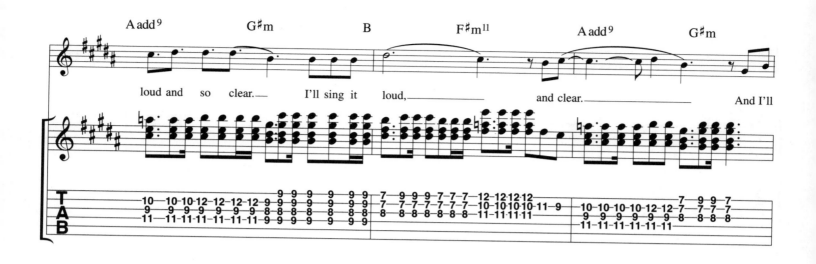

yellow

Words & Music by Guy Berryman, Jon Buckland, Will Champion & Chris Martin

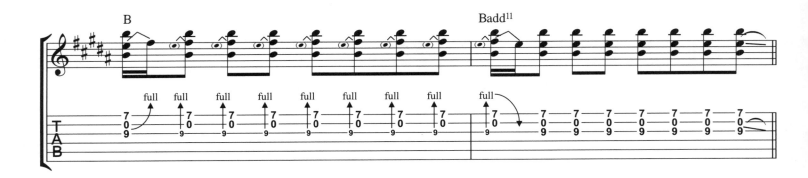

Verse

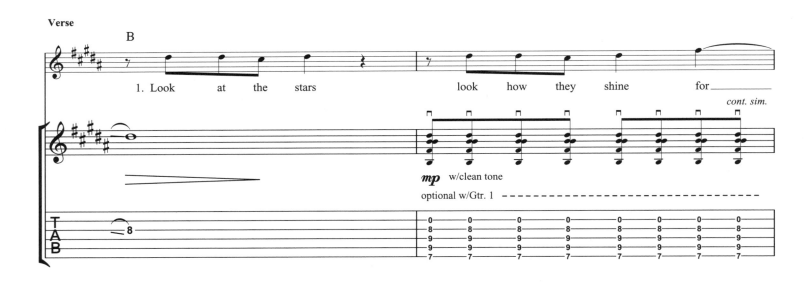

1. Look at the stars look how they shine for

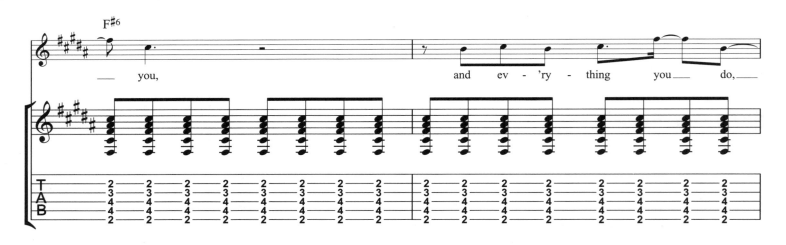

you, and ev - 'ry - thing you do,

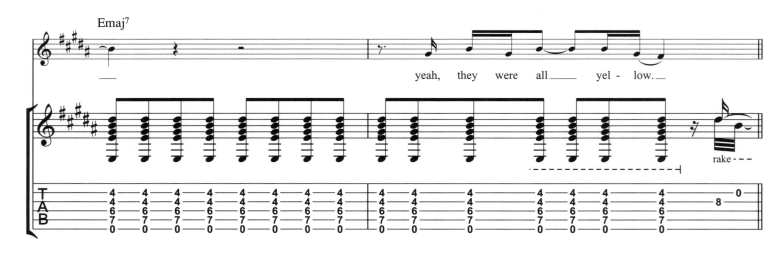

yeah, they were all yel - low.

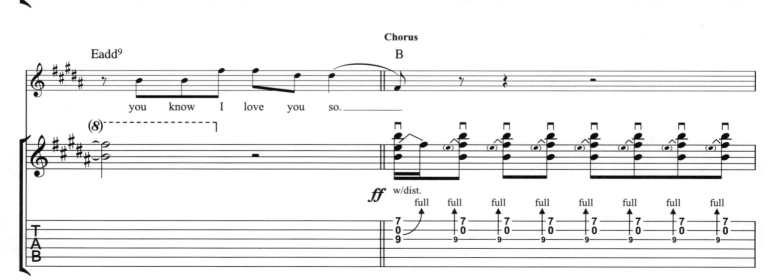

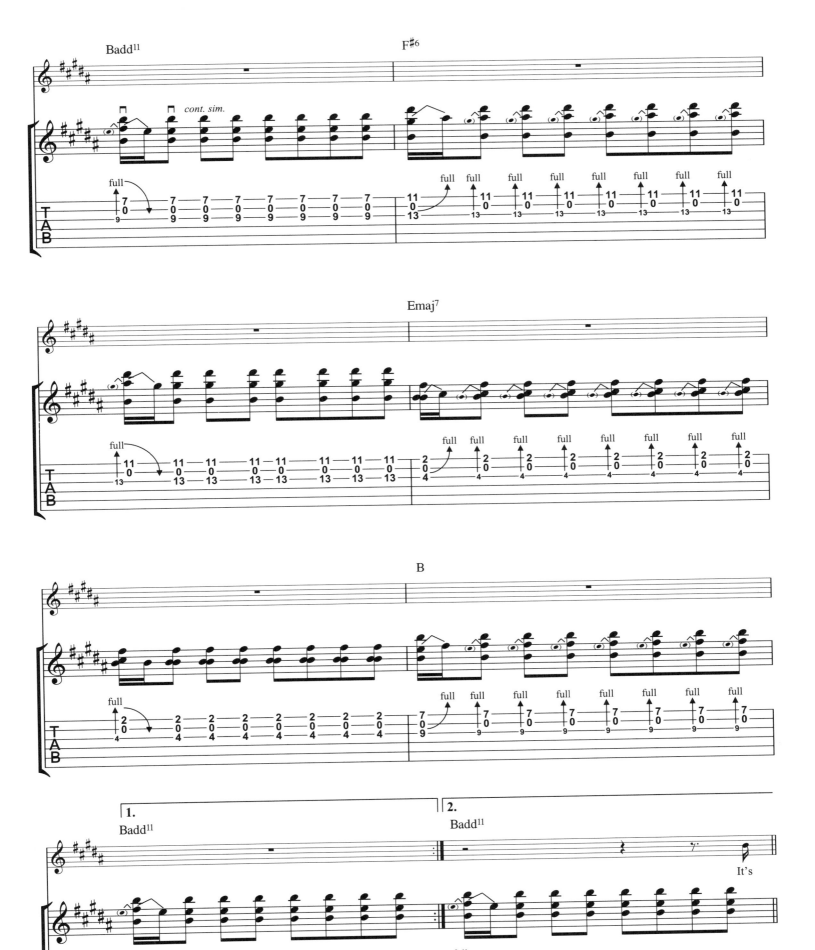

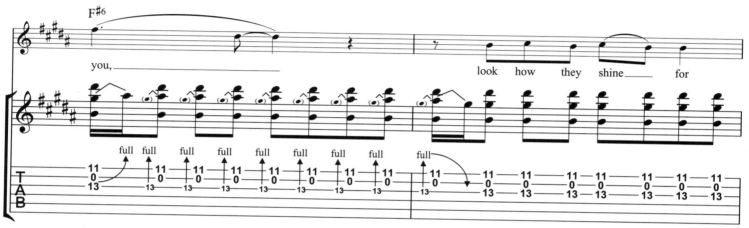

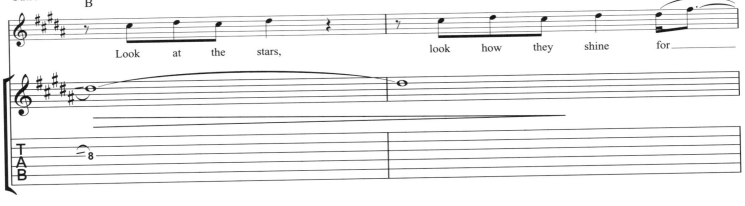

a whisper

Words & Music by Guy Berryman, Jon Buckland, Will Champion & Chris Martin

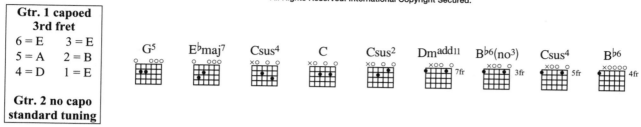

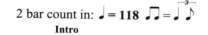

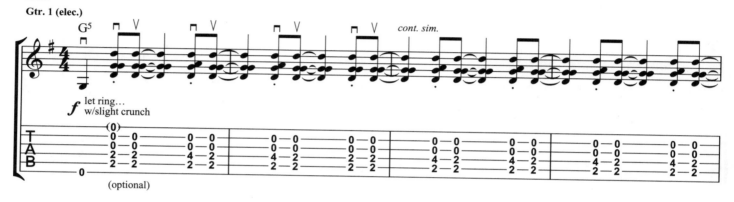

A whis-per,___ a whis-per,___ a whis-per___ a whis-per.___

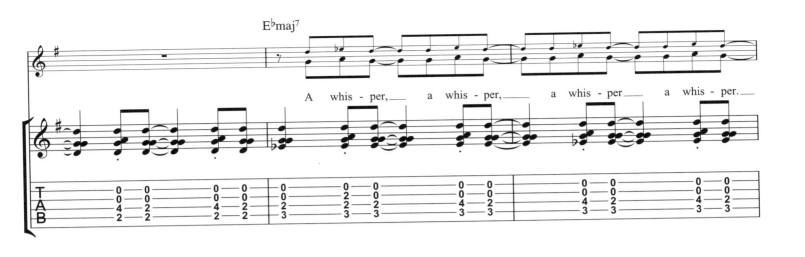

A whis - per, a whis - per, a whis - per a whis - per.

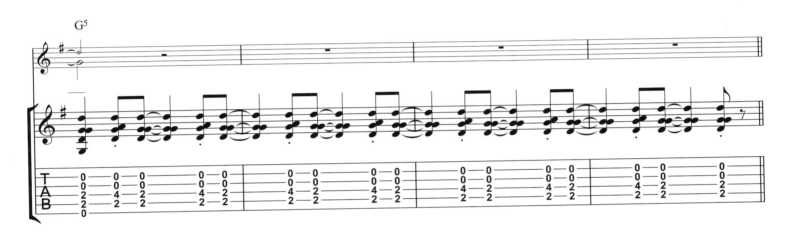

Verse 𝄋

I hear the sound of the tick - ing of clocks, re - mem - ber your face so re -

Gtr. 1

Gtr. 2 (elec.)

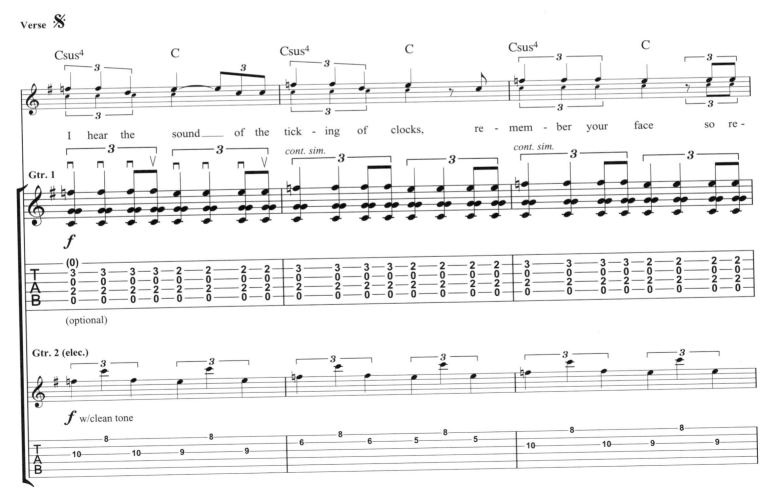

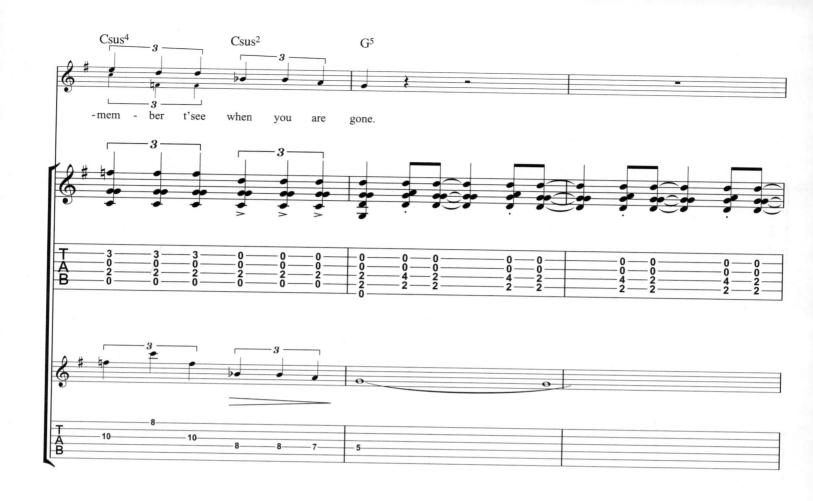

-mem - ber t'see when you are gone.

1° only

I hear the sound____ of the

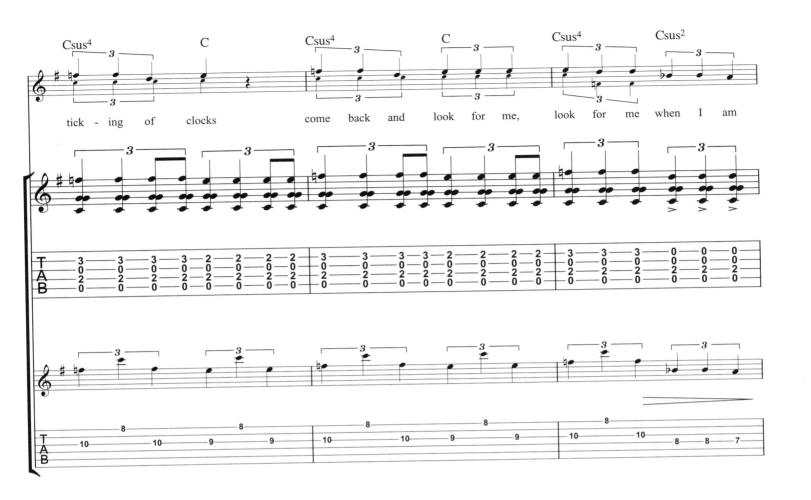

ticking of clocks come back and look for me, look for me when I am

Chorus

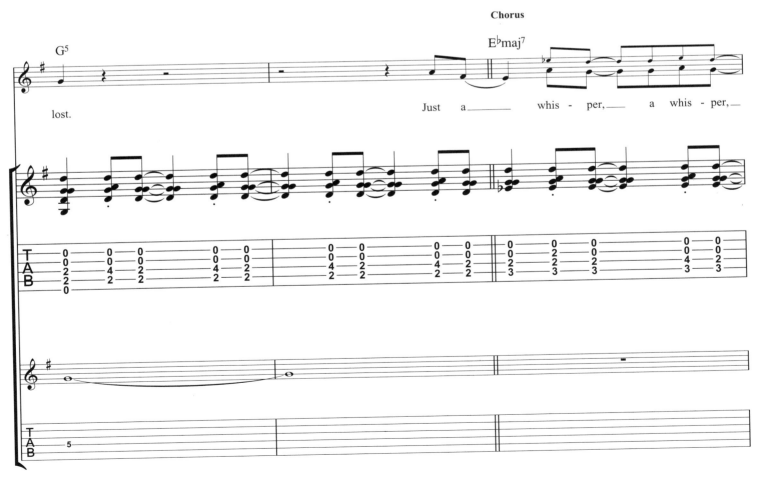

lost.

Just a_____ whis - per,_____ a whis - per,_____

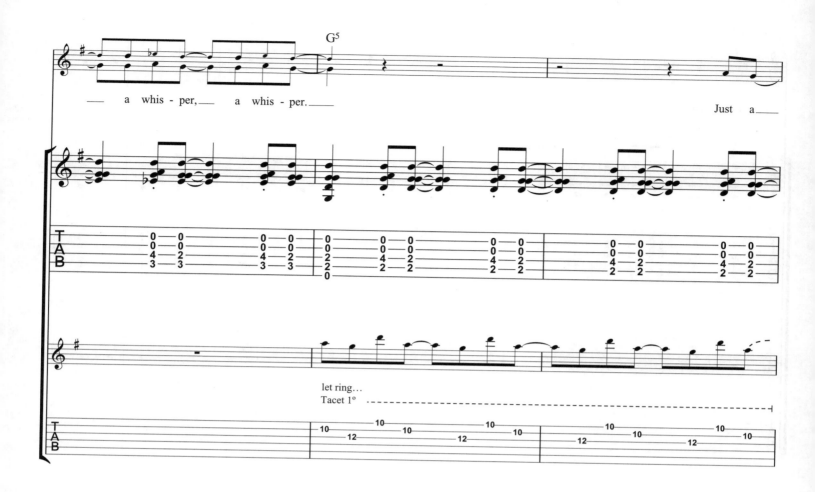

a whis - per,___ a whis - per.___ Just a___

let ring…
Tacet 1°

___ whis - per,___ a whis - per,___ a whis - per,___ a whis - per.___

Bridge

Night_____ turns to day_____ when I___ still___ had these ques - tions._____

*optional w/marimba

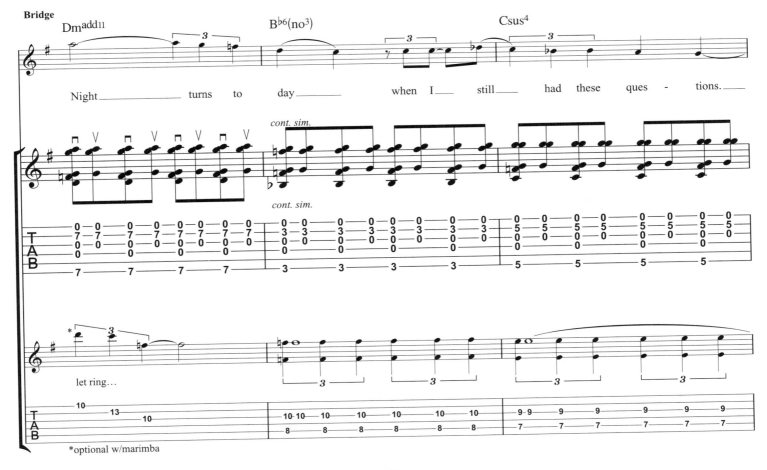

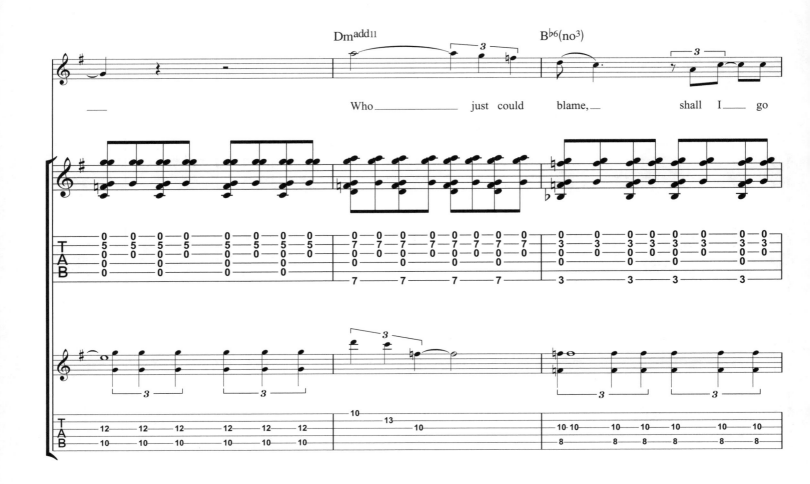

Who _____ just could blame, _____ shall I _____ go

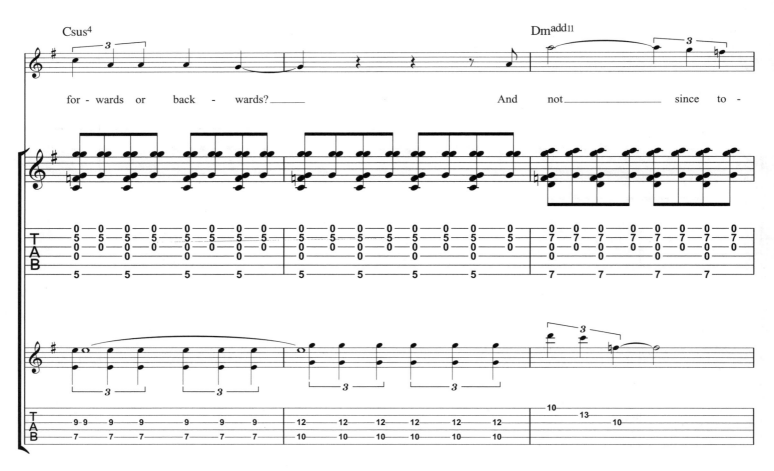

for - wards or back - wards? _____ And not_____ since to -

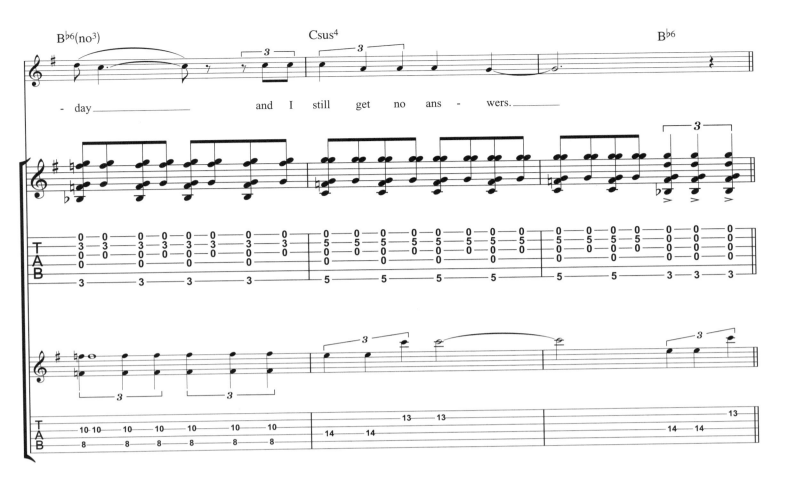

-day _____ and I still get no ans - wers. _____

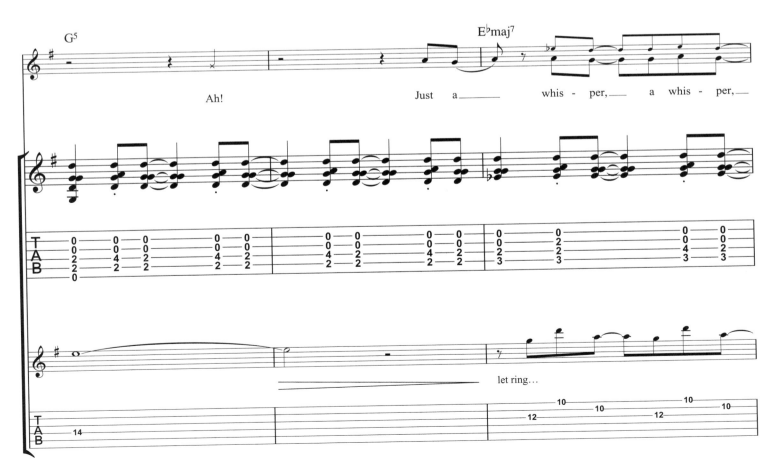

Ah!

Just a _____ whis - per, _____ a whis - per, _____

let ring…

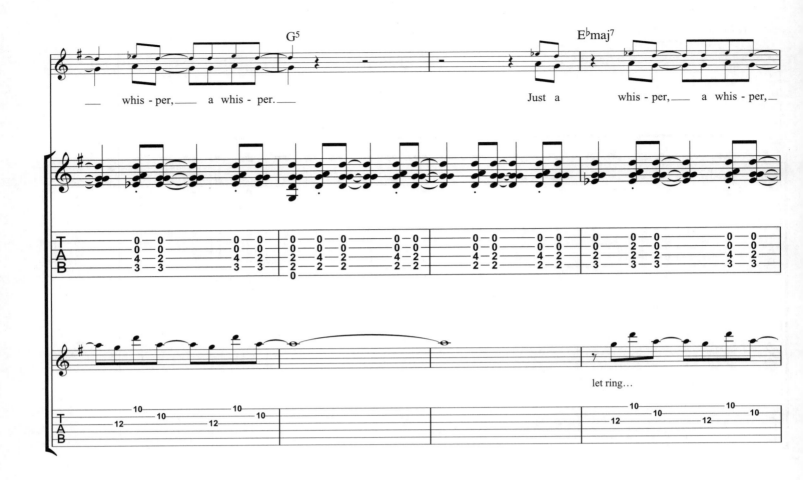

whis - per,____ a whis - per.____   Just a   whis - per,____ a whis - per,____

let ring…

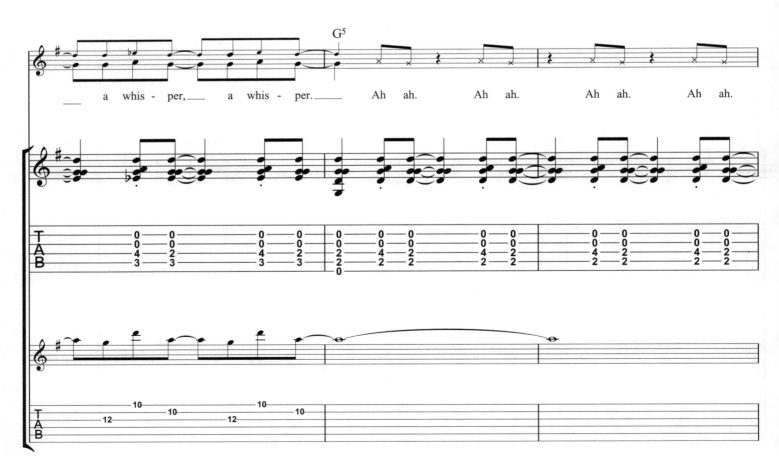

a whis - per,____ a whis - per.____ Ah ah.   Ah ah.   Ah ah.   Ah ah.

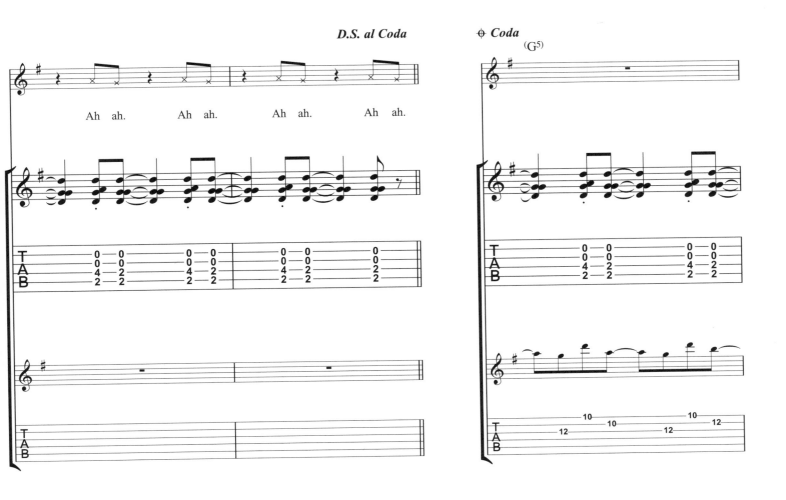

Outro

$B^{\flat 6}(no^3)$ $Csus^4$ G^5 *Repeat to fade*

w/ad lib. vocal to fade

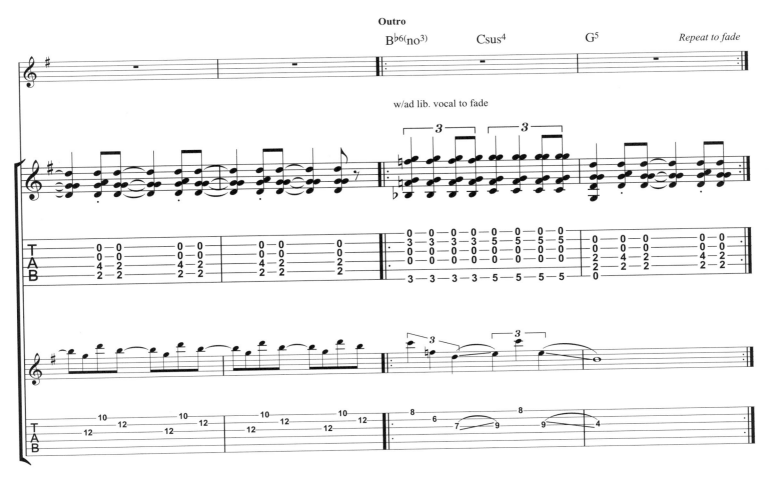

play guitar with...

...the legends of rock - over 60 great book & CD titles to collect

AC/DC
Includes:
back in black
highway to hell
whole lotta rosie
Order No. AM955900

the beatles
Includes:
day tripper
get back
yesterday
Order No. NO90665

the beatles Book 2
Includes:
eight days a week
please please me
ticket to ride
Order No. NO90667

the beatles Book 3
Includes:
here comes the sun
revolution
while my guitar gently weeps
Order No. NO90689

chuck berry
Includes:
around and around
johnny b. goode
no particular place to go
Order No. AM943789

black sabbath
Includes:
iron man
paranoid
war pigs
Order No. AM955911

blur
Includes:
country house
girls and boys
parklife
Order No. AM935320

bon jovi
the early years
Includes:
livin' on a prayer
wanted dead or alive
you give love a bad name
Order No. AM971256

eric clapton
Includes:
layla
sunshine of your love
tears in heaven
Order No. AM950862

phil collins
Includes:
another day in paradise
don't lose my number
one more night
Order No. AM928147

the corrs
Includes:
forgiven, not forgotten
so young
what can i do
Order No. AM960971

the cranberries
Includes:
hollywood
ridiculous thoughts
zombie
Order No. AM941699

dire straits
Includes:
money for nothing
romeo and juliet
sultans of swing
Order No. DG70735

free
Includes:
all right now
fire and water
wishing well
Order No. AM960960

david gilmour
Includes:
learning to fly
on the turning away
take it back
Order No. AM954602

buddy holly
Includes:
rave on
words of love
peggy sue
Order No. AM943734

john lee hooker
Includes:
boom boom
the healer
i'm in the mood
Order No. AM951885

b.b. king
Includes:
every day i have the blues
rock me baby
the thrill is gone
Order No. AM951874

the kinks
Includes:
all day and all of the night
waterloo sunset
you really got me
Order No. AM951863

kula shaker
Includes:
govinda
hey dude
hush
Order No. AM943767

john lennon
Includes:
cold turkey
happy xmas (war is over)
woman
Order No. AM943756

bob marley
Includes:
i shot the sheriff
jamming
no woman, no cry
Order No. AM937739

metallica
Includes:
enter sandman
fade to black
the unforgiven
Order No. AM92559

metallica Book 2
Includes:
creeping death
seek and destroy
whiskey in the jar
Order No. AM955977

alanis morissette
Includes:
hand in my pocket
ironic
you oughta know
Order No. AM943723

oasis
Includes:
cigarettes & alcohol
morning glory
supersonic
Order No. AM935330

ocean colour scene
Includes:
the circle
the day we caught the train
the riverboat song
Order No. AM943712

elvis presley
Includes:
all shook up
blue suede shoes
hound dog
Order No. AM937090

pulp
Includes:
common people
disco 2000
sorted for e's & wizz
Order No. AM938124

the rolling stones
Includes:
brown sugar
(i can't get no) satisfaction
jumpin' jack flash
Order No. AM90247

stereophonics
Includes:
just looking
pick a part that's new
the bartender & the thief
Order No. AM960950

sting
Includes:
an englishman in new york
fields of gold
if you love somebody
  set them free
Order No. AM928092

the stone roses
Includes:
i am the resurrection
i wanna be adored
ten storey love song
Order No. AM943701

the stone roses Book 2
Includes:
fool's gold
love spreads
one love
Order No. AM955890

suede
Includes:
animal nitrate
electricity
we are the pigs
Order No. AM955955

paul weller
Includes:
the changingman
out of the sinking
wild wood
Order No. AM937827

the who
Includes:
i can see for miles
pinball wizard
substitute
Order No. AM955867

the 60's
Includes:
all along the watchtower
  (jimi hendrix)
born to be wild (steppenwolf)
not fade away (the rolling sto...
Order No. AM957748

the 70's
Includes:
all right now (free)
hotel california (the eagles)
live and let die (wings)
Order No. AM957759

the 80's
Includes:
addicted to love (robert palm...
need you tonight (inxs)
where the streets have no
  name (u2)
Order No. AM957760

the 90's
Includes:
everything must go
  (manic street preachers)
love is the law (the seahorses...
wonderwall (oasis)
Order No. AM957770

blues legends
Includes:
crossroads blues (cream)
couldn't stand the weather
  (stevie ray vaughan)
killing floor (jimi hendrix)
Order No. AM958507

classic tracks
Includes:
every breath you take (the po...
hey joe (jimi hendrix)
ziggy stardust (david bowie)
Order No. AM961004

pop anthems
Includes:
angels (robbie williams)
road rage (catatonia)
what can i do (the corrs)
Order No. AM960982

the metal album
Includes:
fade to black (metallica)
live and let die (guns n' roses...
love bites (def leppard)
Order No. AM954426

the gold book
Includes:
johnny b. goode (chuck berry...
layla (eric clapton)
sultans of swing (dire straits...
Order No. AM951907

the platinum book
Includes:
a design for life (manic street...
  preachers)
cigarettes & alcohol (oasis)
the riverboat song
  (ocean colour scene)
Order No. AM951918

...and many more!

play *acoustic guitar with...*

Play guitar or sing along with the CD 'soundalike' backing tracks on all these great titles!

Every song in the music book is presented in easy-to-read guitar tablature with chord symbols and full lyrics

David Bowie *AM967109*
Eric Clapton *AM965954*
Bob Dylan *AM955999*
David Gray *AM970838*
Cat Stevens *AM976767*
Paul Simon *PS11469*
Simon & Garfunkel *PS11516*

20 Great Hits *AM976734*
Includes songs from Oasis, The Beatles,
Elvis Presley & The Who

CD track listing

1 tuning notes

Full instrumental performances (with guitar)...

2 don't panic

3 high speed

4 in my place

5 god put a smile upon your face

6 shiver

7 yellow

8 a whisper

All tracks:
(Berryman/Buckland/Champion/Martin)
BMG Music Publishing Limited.

Backing tracks only (without guitar).

9 don't panic

10 high speed

11 in my place

12 god put a smile upon your face

13 shiver

14 yellow

15 a whisper

MCF

To remove your CD from the plastic sleeve, lift the small lip on the right to break the perforated flap. Replace the disc after use for convenient storage.